Key Stage 2

Punctuation

Carol Matchett

Name   Andy Lin

Schofield & Sims

Introduction

Punctuation shows which words go together to form chunks of meaning. This helps the reader to understand the exact sense of what is written.

In this book, you will find information on all the main punctuation marks, starting with basic sentence punctuation and ending with more complex punctuation, such as colons and semicolons. You will also learn more about writing sentences, because understanding how sentences work helps you understand when and why punctuation is needed.

Finding your way around this book

Before you start using this book, write your name in the name box on the first page.

Then decide how to begin. If you want a complete course on punctuation, you should work right through the book from beginning to end. Another way to use the book is to dip into it when you want to find out about a particular topic, such as apostrophes. The Contents page will help you to find the pages you need.

Whichever way you choose, don't try to do too much at once – it's better to work through the book in short bursts.

When you have found the topic you want to study, look out for these icons, which mark different parts of the text.

This icon shows you the activities that you should complete. You write your answers in the spaces provided. After you have worked through all the activities on the page, turn to pages 38 to 48 to check your answers. When you are sure that you understand the topic, put a tick in the box beside it on the Contents page.

On page 37 you will find suggestions for some projects (**Now you try**), which will give you even more opportunities to improve your understanding of punctuation.

Explanation

This text explains the topic and gives examples. Make sure you read it before you start the activities.

This text gives you useful background information about the subject.

Contents

Explanation

Full stops and capital letters are used to show where sentences start and end. You put a **capital letter** at the **start of a sentence** and a **full stop** at the **end**.

Sentence punctuation is particularly important when you are writing **more than one** sentence.

Example We went to the party. It was great fun.

        end of the first sentence   **start** of the second sentence

Activities

1 Read each line. Decide if it should be **one sentence or two** separate sentences. Add the **capital letters** and **full stops** needed.

    a the old man waited the bus was very late

    b triangles have three sides and squares have four

    c the sky was blue it was a lovely day

    d the boy was late his teacher was angry

    e my best friend is 11 and I am nearly 10

    f ducks have webbed feet to help them swim

2 Complete these sentences and in each case add a second sentence of your own. Remember the full stops and capital letters for **both** sentences.

    a The firefighters _have bright red suits. The suits look like fire._

    b A man appeared carrying _a large bag. It had lots of shopping inside._

    c Cinderella _is my sister's favourite book. However, I detest it_

    d Plants need _lots of water to help them grow. Otherwise, they will die_

Explanation

If you **miss out** capital letters and full stops, it can be **confusing**. Your reader will not know where a sentence begins and ends.

Example Everyone ran outside the house opposite was on fire. **?**

This is confusing – it is not clear if 'everyone ran outside the house' or if 'the house opposite was on fire'. When a full stop and a capital letter are added, the meaning becomes clear.

Example Everyone ran outside. **T**he house opposite was on fire. ✓

Activities

1 In these examples, the writers have forgotten to use **full stops** and **capital letters** between sentences. See if you can insert them. The first one has been started for you.

a
M
my older sister likes to play very loud music. M my little sister spends all her time glued to the television or reading comics.

b
W
we are having a lovely time. T the weather has been great all week.

c
Anil walked towards the door. H he felt the rusty handle the door was locked.

d
M many trees lose their leaves in autumn. T this helps the tree to survive the winter.

e
Sunny Sands has many exciting places for you to visit. A a great place to start is the beach with its many attractions.

Did you know?

The word '**punctuation**' comes from the Latin word 'punctu' meaning 'point'. The first punctuation marks were small dots made with the point of the pen. They told the reader where to pause. To begin with, punctuation was called 'pointing', in English.

Questions and question marks

Some sentences are **questions**. Questions **ask something** and usually need a response.

When writing a question, you need to put a **question mark** at the end to show your reader that the sentence is a question.

Example Who is your favourite singer**?** ← question mark as shown

Activities

1 Some of these sentences are questions. If the sentence asks a **question** change the full stop to a **question mark**.

a How do you feel today   **?**

b Is this your dog   **?**

c You will really like this new game **.**

d Why does the wind blow   **?**

e I can swim a length of the pool **.**

f Do you think we can win this match **?**

2 Write some **questions** you might ask a new pupil at your school, beginning with the words below. Remember to use question marks.

a What do _you like to play during break?_

b Where did _you go on holiday in the summer?_

c When is _your birthday._

d Why have _you got a Minecraft backpack?_

e How many _siblings do you have?_

Did you know?

Hundreds of years ago, most texts were read aloud. Scribes (or writers) needed a way of telling the readers when to change their voices to make it sound like a question. First they put the letter 'q' (for 'question' or 'quaestio' in Latin), followed by a dot. This eventually became the question mark.

Exclamations and exclamation marks

Explanation

You can add an **exclamation mark** to a sentence that needs more **impact**. For example, you might want to show **strong feelings** such as surprise, excitement, fear or anger.

The exclamation mark tells the reader how to read the sentence (in a loud or an excited voice).

Example I had won a million pounds**!**   He landed with a huge splash**!**

Activities

1 Read these sentences and decide the most suitable final punctuation. Put a **full stop** or an **exclamation mark** in each box. (Use each punctuation style three times.)

a   I went to school   `.`

b   Suddenly everyone shouted HAPPY BIRTHDAY   `!`

c   My best friend lives in the house next door   `.`

d   My best friend has dyed her hair bright pink   `!`

e   Great prizes to be won   `!`

f   Sweets are bad for your teeth   `.`

2 Here are some **exclamations** – short words or phrases that express strong emotions or feelings. Copy the right exclamation into each of the speech bubbles.

> **Help!**   **Ouch!**   **Oh dear!**   **What a mess!**

a

b

c

d

Did you know?

In Spanish, upside down question marks and exclamation marks are used at the beginning of questions and exclamations.

Example ¡Qué sorpresa! ('What a surprise!')   ¿Qué desean? ('What would you like?')

Other uses of capital letters

Activities

1 Complete these sentences using **capital letters** in the right places.

My name is ___Andy Zhe Lin.___ . I live in ___London.___ .

My birthday is in ___October.___ . My teacher is ___Mr Dumas.___ .

My favourite television programme is ___Dream Speedrunner.___ .

2 These sentences have capital letters missing. Insert them in the correct places. The first one has been done for you.

a Turn right into Cedar Road and walk as far as St George's School.

b Meet Tess outside Spendless Supermarket on Monday.

c Amelia Earhart flew across the Atlantic Ocean in May 1932.

d The author Philip Ridley was born in London. As well as being an author, he is

also an artist. He studied painting at St Martin's School of Art. Some of his most

famous books are *Meteorite Spoon*, *Krindlekrax* and *Mercedes Ice*.

Proofreading 1

Explanation

You should always read through your writing to check for any mistakes. This is called **proofreading**. Always check that you have used **sentence punctuation** correctly. This means checking for **full stops**, **capital letters**, **question marks** and **exclamation marks**.

Read 'aloud' in your head so that you can hear where the sentences start and end.

Activities

1 **Proofread** this letter and add the missing **sentence punctuation**.

Dear Alice,

thank you for the birthday card I am sorry to hear about your cold are you feeling

better now You missed a great party on saturday shall I tell you about it We had a

disco in the garden and then a barbecue everyone joined in with dancing on the

grass the funniest moment was when ben stokes fell in the pond It was hilarious

2 Now proofread this advert for a new breakfast cereal.

Are you fed up with the same boring breakfast cereal then try new frosty fruity

flakes It's the fruit with a crunch you will simply love these golden flakes of

crunchy corn they come packed with the flavour of real fruit and taste just

great Go on, start your day with a true fruit boost

Did you know?

The term '**proofreading**' comes from printing, where the first rough copy is called the proof. When books were first printed in the fifteenth century, people realised a fixed set of punctuation marks was needed. Before then, everyone made up their own marks! So printers invented the punctuation marks we still use today.

Commas in lists

Activities

1 Insert **commas** between the items listed in these sentences.

a For a healthy start to the day, try having fruit juice, low sugar cereal, wholemeal toast and some fresh fruit.

b You will need two pieces of card, a sharp pencil, some glue, felt tip pens, and a pair of scissors.

c Try adding grated cheese slices of pepper mushrooms, chopped ham, and sweetcorn to the top of your pizza.

d The book includes short stories from famous authors such as Nina Bawden, Michael Morpurgo, Rose Impey and Joan Aiken.

e Leo's lost kitten was not in the kitchen, the living room, the garage or the cupboard under the stairs.

Commas are also used to **separate** lists of other words such as **adjectives** or **verbs**.

Example The biggest, ugliest, hairiest spider in the world.
The waves came pounding, rushing, scurrying onto the beach.

2 Complete these sentences by adding a **list** of interesting items. Remember to use commas.

a In the old lady's handbag there was _a leather diary, some perfume, a mysterious bottle and a green wallet._

b In the treasure chest we found _gold bars, diamond rings, ruby necklace and amethyst rings._

c On planet Zelg we saw _five-legged aliens, floating buildings and upside-down trees_

Apostrophes: omission

Explanation

Sometimes two words are run together to make a **contraction** (or **shortened form**) of the words.

Example do not → don't ← apostrophe

In this example, an **apostrophe** goes where the letter 'o' would be.

An **apostrophe** is used to show where a **letter has been missed out**. Sometimes the apostrophe replaces more than one missing letter.

Activities

1 Write a **contraction** (or shortened form) of these words. Use an **apostrophe** in place of the missing letter or letters. The first one has been done for you.

a is not → _isn't_

b I had → _I'd_

c should not → _shouldn't_

d we have → _we've_

e does not → _doesn't_

f you are → _you're_

g I will → _I'll_

h Jenna is → _Jenna's_

2 Here is some dialogue from a story. Make the dialogue sound more natural by writing a contraction in place of the crossed-out words. Remember to use apostrophes to replace missing letters.

'Kavita! ~~I have~~ _I've_ been looking everywhere for you,' exclaimed Michael.

'Come on, ~~we will~~ _we'll_ have to run. ~~It is~~ _It's_ late.'

'~~I am~~ _I'm_ not running. I ~~do not~~ _don't_ care if ~~we are~~ _we're_ late,' said Kavita in disgust.

'~~It will~~ _It'll_ be your fault if we miss the start of the concert. ~~They have~~ _They've_

probably started already. We promised ~~we would~~ _we'd_ be there.'

We often use contractions in speech and in informal writing. But you should not use them in more formal writing.

Example **Do not** disturb the animals ← official sign

 Don't disturb the animals ← spoken (perhaps by a parent or teacher)

Apostrophes: possession

Explanation

The **possessive apostrophe** is used to show when **something belongs to someone** or something.

Example the bag belonging to Micha → Micha**'s** bag.

's goes after the name of the person the item belongs to. It is shorter to write 'Micha's bag' than 'the bag belonging to Micha'.

Activities

1 Rewrite each of these phrases using an **apostrophe**. The first one has been done for you.

    a the teeth belonging to the monster → *the monster's teeth*

    b the beanstalk belonging to Jack → *Jack's beanstalk*

    c the CDs belonging to Tarik → *Tarik's CDs*

    d the walls of the castle → *the castle's walls*

    e the first book of the author → *the author's first book*

If the owner is **plural** and the word already **ends –s**, you add the apostrophe **after the –s**.

Example the coats belonging to **the boys** → the **boys'** coats

But some plurals don't end –s, so then you add **'s** as usual.

Example the cloakroom for **women** → the **women's** cloakroom

2 Write phrases to show **which items belong** to **which group** of people. One has been done for you.

~~shorts~~	~~uniforms~~	~~playground~~	~~hats~~	~~staffroom~~	~~surgery~~
~~childrens~~	~~doctors~~	~~footballers~~	~~teachers~~	~~chefs~~	~~soldiers~~

    the chefs' hats   *the doctors' set-surgery*

    the teacher's staffroom   *the footballers' shorts*

    the children's playground   *the soldiers' uniforms*

Apostrophes: confusions

Explanation

Sometimes the **possessive apostrophe** (**'s**) is confused with the **–s** on the end of a plural noun.

Example For sale – book's and toy's ✗ ← plurals
For sale – book**s** and toy**s** ✓

Never use **s'** or **'s** to form plurals – plurals just end **–s**. Only use apostrophes in place of **missing letters** (see page 11) or to show **possession** (see page 12).

Activities

1 All these signs have **apostrophe errors**. Write the signs correctly.

a DVD's for sale _DVDs for sale_

b Jeans café _Jean's café_

c No camera's allowed _No cameras allowed_

d Teas and coffee's _Teas and coffees_

e childrens' clothe's _childrens clothes_

f Opens Sunday's _Opens Sundays_

g Stellas cupcakes _Stella's cupcakes_

h Teds taxi's _Ted's taxis_

Possessive pronouns (mine, ours, yours, his, hers, theirs, its) already show possession, so an **apostrophe is not needed**.

Example That coat is her**'s**. ✗ This one is your**'s**. ✗
That coat is **hers**. ✓ This one is **yours**. ✓

---

2 There is an apostrophe error in each of the sentences below. Underline the error and write the correction.

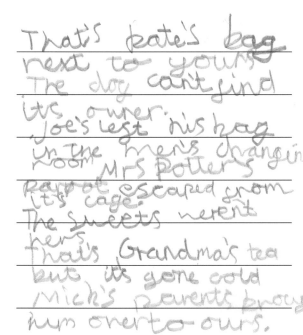

a That's Kates bag next to yours.

That's Kate's bag next to yours

b The dog can't find it's owner.

The dog can't find its owner.

c Joe's left his bag in the mens changing room.

Joe's left his bag in the men's changing room

d Mrs Potter's parrot escaped from it's cage.

Mrs Potter's parrot escaped from its cage.

e The sweets weren't her's.

The sweets weren't hers.

f That's Grandma's tea but its gone cold.

That's Grandma's tea but it's gone cold

g Micks parents brought him over to ours.

Mick's parents brought him over to ours.

Inverted commas 1

Explanation

Inverted commas (or speech marks) are used in **direct speech** to show the words that are actually spoken. You put the inverted commas at the **start** and **end** of the **spoken words**. Any words that are **not spoken** go **outside** the inverted commas.

Example 'I'll meet you later,' called Bill.

          spoken   *not* spoken   (verb and speaker)

A **comma** is used at the **end** of the **spoken words** to **separate** the spoken and non-spoken words. The comma goes **inside** the **inverted commas**. If the spoken words end with a **question mark** or an **exclamation mark**, use this instead of the comma.

Activities

1   Take the words from the speech bubbles and write them as **direct speech** using **inverted commas**. The first one has been done for you.

a

Simeon

That was fun!

'That was fun!' exclaimed Simeon.

b

Maya

Aah, peace at last.

"Aah, peace at last," said Maya.

c

Mr Jenkins

What do you think you're doing?

"What do you think you're doing?" bellowed Mr Jenkins

d

Kelly

We will have to jump!

"We will have to jump!" whimpered Kelly.

Inverted commas 2

Sometimes the **spoken words** are placed at the **end** of the sentence. **Inverted commas** still go round the spoken words and the **end punctuation** still goes **inside** the inverted commas.

Example   The secretary glanced up and asked**,** 'Can I help you**?**'
Max smiled politely and replied**,** 'Yes, I am looking for Mr Khan**.**'

comma
(separating the spoken and
non-spoken words)

end punctuation

Activities

1   Rewrite the sentences from page 14, putting the **spoken words** at the **end** of the sentence. The first one has been done for you.

a   <u>Simeon exclaimed, 'That was fun!'</u>

b   <u>Maya said, " Aah, peace at Last."</u>

c   <u>Mr Jenkins bellowed," What do you think you're doing"</u>

d   <u>Kelly whimpered " We will have to Jump!"</u>

2   Insert the **missing punctuation** in these lines of dialogue.

a   Mr Henderson asked Are we ready to go?

b   Suddenly, a voice shouted Look out below

c   Where are you going asked Ellie. It will be dark soon,

d   The captain announced We sail tomorrow.

e   It's nearly home time said Miss Achebe. Let's tidy up,

f   Sam shouted Wait for me as he ran after the bus.

The **first letter** inside the inverted commas is usually a **capital** letter. But if the words spoken are **interrupted in mid-sentence** then reopen the direct speech with a **lower case** letter.

Example   'This afternoon,' announced Mr Williams, '**w**e have a special visitor.'

Setting out direct speech

Explanation

As well as using inverted commas, an important rule to remember when writing **direct speech** is to **start a new line** each time a **new person** starts to speak.

Example 'We can't sell Daisy. She is all we have,' groaned **Jack**.
'We must sell her,' replied **his mother**, 'or we shall surely starve.'

Activities

1. This is a conversation that takes place in the story *Jack and the Beanstalk*.

> The old woman asked Jack if he could spare a few coins so that she could buy a little bread for her supper. Jack explained that he too was very poor and Daisy the cow was all that he had.
>
> Then Jack had an idea … he told the old lady that she could have the cow to take to market.
>
> The old lady refused at first, but Jack insisted.
>
> Finally the old lady agreed to take the cow, but only if Jack would take the magic beans she offered in return.

Write the conversation as **direct speech**, using **inverted commas** and **other punctuation** where it is needed. **Start a new line** for each change of speaker. The first sentence has been done for you.

'Excuse me, young man, but can you spare a few coins so that I can buy a little bread for my supper?' croaked the old lady.
"Sorry I'm too poor." explained Jack, " All I have is a cow."
Soon he said " Wait you can take the cow."
"I Refuse" the lady said at first but after She excepted If he took some magic beans.

An **ellipsis (…)** is used to show that a sentence is **incomplete** or that something has been **missed out**. It is often used in direct speech to show an interruption or speech trailing off. It is sometimes used in stories to create a dramatic pause – as above in *Jack and the Beanstalk*.

Proofreading 2

1 Write a letter in the box to show whether the **apostrophe** in each sentence is used for **omission (O)** or **possession (P)**.

a We're too busy. `P`

b I am Marie's best friend. `O`

c It was his father's voice. `O`

d Zoe's forgotten me. `O`

e She's late again. `O`

f Look in the dog's basket. `O`

2 Which of these sentences is punctuated **correctly**? Tick the box.

a 'Suddenly, a voice shouted! Everyone get down.' ☐

b Suddenly, a voice shouted, 'Everyone get down!' ☑

c Suddenly, a voice shouted, 'Everyone get down'! ☐

3 **Proofread** this passage of **direct speech**. Add or insert any **missing punctuation**.

"When did you have it last?" asked Lara.

"I'm not sure," said Guy, searching through his pockets.

"Perhaps it's at Simon's house?" suggested Max.

"I don't think so," said Guy. I never took it out.

"Can you remember dropping it?" asked Max.

"Got it," shouted Guy, holding up a key. "It must've dropped through the lining."

4 Insert the **three** missing **commas** in the sentence below.

Gran wore a checked woollen skirt, a flowery blouse, a pink cardigan, a patterned headscarf and blue fluffy slippers.

Commas: separation 1

Explanation

Commas are used to separate words, phrases and clauses **within a sentence.** We use a comma when an **adverb** or **adverbial phrase** is placed at the **start** of a sentence. The comma **separates** the adverbial from the main sentence.

Example However, this was not really what happened.
In my opinion, it was the wrong decision.

Activities

1 Rewrite each sentence, moving the **adverbial** (in **bold**) to the beginning of the sentence and adding a **comma.**

a I woke **slowly** from a deep sleep.   Slowly, I woke from a deep sl

b Attach the string **next.**   Next, attach the string.

c The sun came out **suddenly.**   Suddenly, the sun came out.

d The rain has **finally** stopped.   Finally, the rain has stopped

e It worked out fine **anyway.**   Anyway it worked out fi

f We leave for Spain **tomorrow.**   Tomorrow, we leave for Spai

g She **eagerly** opened the box.   Eagerly, she opened the box

2 Complete each sentence by choosing an **adverbial** from the box. Insert a **comma** to separate the phrase from the rest of the sentence.

a On Saturday morning   the family went shopping.

b Before the concert   the orchestra tuned up.

c On holiday   we swam every day.

d In last night's gale   all the bins blew over.

e At five o'clock   the coach will leave London.

f By the next morning   the storm was over.

| On holiday | Before the concert | By the next morning |
| In last night's gale | On Saturday morning | At 5 o'clock |

Commas: separation 2

Explanation

Commas are used to **separate** words and phrases that appear at the **start or end of a sentence**. These might be a commenting phrase, the name of the person being spoken to, or words like 'yes' and 'no'.

Example I cannot help you, **I'm afraid**.
          Marie, can you come here?

Activities

1 Put the **commas** in these sentences.

a No, that can't be right.

b Stella, is that you?

c Ah well, that's my work done for today.

d Yes, he was sure this was the place.

e You can stop that right now, Martin.

f Oh dear, we seem to have forgotten something.

g Sarah and Michael, I'm talking to you.

Sometimes a **sentence** is turned into a question by adding a **question tag**. A **comma** is used to **separate** the question tag from the main sentence.

Example She's very brave, **isn't she?** ◄— question tag

---

2 Turn these statements into questions by adding **question tags**. (Remember to use a **comma**). The first one has been done for you.

a He's very late, _isn't he?_

b That's a beautiful sight, isn't it?

c They are the best team, isn't it?

d We will win, won't we?

e You do believe me, don't you?

f You're Ben's friend, aren't you?

Commas: subordinate clauses 1

Explanation

Some **sentences** have a **main clause** followed by a **subordinate clause**. Subordinate clauses often start with **conjunctions** like 'when' or 'because'.

Example The car suddenly stopped, **when** it hit the lamppost.

↑   ↑

main clause   subordinate clause

You usually **don't need a comma** in a sentence like this, where the conjunction clearly joins the two parts together. But with some conjunctions a comma *is* needed to help make the meaning clear.

Activities

1   Rewrite each pair of sentences as **one sentence**, using the **conjunction** shown in red.

a   Marcia watched the world become smaller. She zoomed into the sky.   **as**

Marcia watched the world become smaller as she zoomed into the sky.

b   The box was heavy. It was only small.   **although**

The box was heavy although. It was only small

c   Henry VIII was King of England from 1509. He died in 1547.   **until**

Henry VIII was King of England from 1509. He died in 1547.

d   It is important to eat lots of fruit and vegetables. They contain vitamins.   **because**

It is important to eat lots of fruit and vegetables because they contain vitamins.

e   Carrie paused for a moment. Then she entered the room.   **before**

Carrie paused for a moment before she entered the room.

2   Insert a **comma** after the **main clause** in these sentences.

a   Stacey enjoys all sports, especially playing tennis.

b   Max was late, which really annoyed James.

c   Everyone agreed to try, yet no-one wanted to go first.

Did you know?

The word '**comma**' comes from the Greek word 'komma', meaning a part of a sentence (like a phrase or a clause). Only later was the word used for the punctuation mark itself.

Commas: subordinate clauses 2

Activities

9:04 9:14

1 Rewrite each sentence, moving the **subordinate clause** (in **bold**) to the **start** of the sentence. Remember to use a **comma** to separate the two clauses.

a I escaped from the aliens **when the spaceship landed**.

I escaped from the aliens, when the spaceship landed.

b We will have to stay inside **if it rains all day**.

We will have to stay inside, if it rains allday.

c The journey took longer than expected **because the roads were flooded**.

The journey took longer than expected, because the roads were flooded

d We were soon completely lost **although I had a map**.

We were soon completely lost, although I had a map.

e They continued to hunt for survivors **as darkness fell**.

They continued to hunt for survivours, as darkness fell.

2 Complete the subordinate clause at the start of each sentence. Use a comma to separate the two parts of the sentence.

a While _we partied_ , your dog ate the birthday cake.

b When _I got home_ , I went to bed.

c As _somebody spoke_ , everyone looked up.

d Although _he wanted to go on his own_ , he followed the others.

Commas: subordinate clauses 3

17:06 17:14

Explanation

Subordinate clauses do not always start with a conjunction.

Example <u>Waving his arms wildly</u>, Kofi ran down the street.

subordinate clause ⟶ comma (separating the parts of the sentence)

Here a **verb** (Waving) is used at the **start** of the subordinate clause. When sentences are formed like this, a **comma** is needed to separate the clauses or parts of a sentence.

Activities

1 Complete these sentences. Add a **comma** and a **main clause** (to say what happened at that moment). The first one has been done for you.

a Running frantically, <u>the man shouted for help.</u>

b Grabbing the steering wheel, <u>he swerved out of the cyclist's w</u>

c Trembling nervously, <u>the woman screamed.</u>

d Amazed by what she had seen, <u>she fainted</u>

e Moving cautiously, <u>he escaped the maniac.</u>

f Watched by the others, <u>she darted out of sight</u>

2 Choose a **subordinate clause** from the box to complete each of these sentences. Put a comma between clauses.

a <u>Finding a trail of footprints</u>, Millie followed them.

b <u>Looking through the window</u>, Nick saw everything.

c The clock struck midnight, <u>making Cinderella jump.</u>

d The wind blew fiercely, <u>forcing Hassan back</u>

e The phone rang suddenly, <u>startling Mrs Bishop</u>

> making Cinderella jump   looking through the window
>
> forcing Hassan back   finding a trail of footprints   startling Mrs Bishop

Commas: clarifying meaning

Explanation

Commas are important because they **separate** parts of a sentence. They help make the **meaning clear** and prevent any **ambiguity** or **confusion**. If you do not use commas, your reader might not know what you mean.

Example Watching the monster Jack began to tremble. **?**

This is confusing – it is not clear if the monster is called Jack or if Jack is the one who is beginning to tremble. When a **comma** is added, the meaning becomes clear.

Example Watching the monster**,** Jack began to tremble. ✓

Activities

1 Insert the missing **comma** into each of these sentences to help make the **meaning clear**.

a Standing next to her uncle, Sam felt tiny.

b It must be nearly time to eat, Dad.

c The dragon had large, bright green wings.

d Most of the time, travellers were happy with the service.

e They had 50 model cars each, in its original box.

2 Which **three** of these sentences would be clearer with a comma? Put a tick in those boxes.

a Dad promised he'd come when he finished work. ☑

b Seeing the creature so close Kelly grew anxious. ☑

c Snow fell while we were sleeping. ☐

d Varsha opened the door a little peering into the darkness. ☑

e As it was dark inside the children could see nothing. ☑

> ### Did you know?
> The use of commas is always changing. In the eighteenth century writers used long sentences with commas separating every clause and phrase. Today we use commas only when they are needed to show breaks in sentences and make the meaning clear.

Write the three sentences correctly.

Seeing the creature so close, Kelly grew anxious.

Varsha opened the door a little, peering into the darkness.

As it was dark inside, the children could see nothing.

Commas and full stops

Explanation

Remember, **commas** should only be used **within a sentence**. Commas should not be used between separate sentences. **Between sentences** you must use a **full stop**.

Example Amie made her way through the crowd of people**,** Sheena followed her. ✗

Here the two events should be described in **two separate sentences**.

Example Amie made her way through the crowd of people**.** Sheena followed her. ✓

Activities

1 Check the following examples. If the **comma** has been used **correctly**, put a **tick** in the box. If not, put a **cross** in the box and make the necessary changes.

a Shining the torch into the darkness, Sara could just make out a small figure. ☑

b As soon as she heard the scream, Cal rushed downstairs. ☑

c The man asked Carlos for some help, Carlos ignored him. ☒

d Henry VIII had six wives, Catherine of Aragon was Henry's first wife. ☒

e Looking out of the plane, we could see the patchwork of fields below us. ☑

f Heat the oven to 180°C, place the biscuits on a baking tray. ☒

2 This short extract uses no punctuation. Rewrite it using **full stops**, **capital letters** and **commas** to help make the meaning clear.

glowing fiercely the spaceship hovered just overhead while it was really quite close to us it was almost impossible to see anything because of the light we had to shield our eyes

Glowing fiercely, the spaceship hovered just overhead. While it was really quite close to us, it was almost impossible to see anything. Because of the light, we had to shield our eyes.

Proofreading 3

1 **a** Underline the two words that need **apostrophes**, and write them in.

The boys <u>couldnt</u> find either of <u>Tims</u> sisters.

b Explain why each apostrophe is needed.

The word 'couldnt' needs an apostrophe because its a contraction. 'Tims' needs an apostrophe for possesion

2 Insert **two commas** in the sentence below.

As he passed the school gates, he began thinking about Mrs Walker, Suzie and the other pupils.

3 Rewrite the passage below with the **correct punctuation**.

When I saw the man, coming towards me, I felt afraid, we both stopped waiting for each other to move.

When I saw the man coming towards me, I felt afraid. We both stopped, waiting for each other to move.

4 **Proofread** this passage. Insert the missing punctuation.

"Whats that in your hand?" asked Sadie.

"Nothing," replied Mark, clearly startled.

"Why are you hiding it then?" pressed Sadie, "I know youre up to something."

"Its mine," Mark muttered defensively

"Come on hand it over, little brother," said Sadie, grabbing her brothers clenched fist

Parenthesis: commas

Explanation

Sometimes **extra information** is added into the **middle of a sentence**. This extra information is called a **parenthesis**. It might be a word, a phrase or a subordinate clause. It adds extra detail to the main sentence.

Example Laura, **feeling rather pleased,** put the box back in the sideboard.

Here **two commas** are used to cut off or **separate** the extra information from the main sentence.

Activities

1 Underline the **extra information** that has been added into each of these sentences. Insert the **two commas** needed to separate the information from the main sentence.

a Mr Richardson, the headteacher, was pleased with the response.

b Sheila Jenks, aged 50, was recovering last night in hospital.

c The man, smiling to himself, put the money in his pocket.

d Mrs Patel, who was rather old, had to sit down to rest.

e The cottage, which is empty, stands on the edge of the village.

f Sam, although the youngest, was a worthy winner.

2 Choose a name and a phrase giving extra information from the boxes below to complete each sentence. Use **commas** to separate the **extra information** from the rest of the sentence.

a Mr Reynolds, the teacher, _____ spoke to the class.

b Miss mysical, the magician, _____ performed her vanishing trick.

c Molly, my little sister, _____ is six years old.

d Zoe star, the singer, _____ performed her latest hit.

e Snowflake, the white cat, _____ was stuck in the oak tree.

Name		Phrase	
	Molly		the teacher
Mr Reynolds	Miss Mystical	the white cat	the singer
Zoe Star	Snowflake	my little sister	the magician

Parenthesis: brackets

10: 39 10:45

Explanation

Brackets are also used to add an extra piece of information into a sentence. This might be extra detail, a comment, an explanation or even a reference to another part of the text. The brackets go **round the extra information** to separate it from the main sentence.

Example Lenny **(the one with the squeaky voice)** seemed to be in charge.

Two dashes can be used in the same way (see page 28).

Activities

1 Underline the **extra information** that has been added into each of these sentences. Put **brackets** round the information.

a We tried two flavours (orange and strawberry) but didn't like either.

b Animals have to be able to hide from their predators (the animals that hunt them) in order to survive.

c The survey found that most people (almost 70% of those) asked would like to see the playground kept open.

d Make sure you leave a small opening at the top (see Diagram 2).

e All carnivores (meat eaters) have sharp teeth.

f Nikki (who lives next door) rushed to our rescue.

2 Use brackets to add a comment or extra piece of information into these sentences.

a In the bath (Yesterday) was the biggest spider I'd ever seen.

b I have two rabbits (called jumpy and carrot), a dog and a goldfish.

c Ali (as always) was last to finish.

d Mum (without noticing) left the tap running.

e Mr Martin's new car (when I was watching) was stolen on Monday.

f We grew all sorts of vegetables (like carrots and beans) in our garden.

Parenthesis: dashes

11:15   1:25

Explanation

You can use **two dashes** to add an **extra piece of information** into a sentence in the same way as you might use **brackets** or two **commas**. Two dashes are often used in **informal** letters or diaries to add a comment (or an aside) to the main sentence.

Example Tasha – **as always** – was late this morning.

Activities

1 Underline the **extra information** that has been added into each of these sentences. Rewrite each sentence inserting **two dashes**.

a   My father not the greatest cook made pizza for everyone.

My father - not the greatest cook - made pizza for everyone.

b   Just one more lesson PE with Mr Roberts before home time.

Just one more lesson - PE with Mr Roberts - before home time.

c   James who was bored thought it was time to leave.

James - who was bored - thought it was time to leave.

d   The dragon a huge, scaly beast emerged from the cave.

The dragon - a huge, scaly beast - emerged from the cave.

e   His choice of clothes a T-shirt and jeans seemed out of place.

His choice of clothes - a T-shirt and jeans - seemed out of place.

2 Imagine you were writing an **informal** letter or diary. Use two dashes to add a comment, an aside or an extra piece of information to these sentences.

a   Mrs Hopkins – the receptionist – complained about the noise.

b   Jodie – very surprisingly – won the competition.

c   Our new teacher – who is really nice – is called Mr Groves.

d   Dad was in the kitchen – like always – when they arrived.

e   Harry's model – by far – was clearly the best.

Other uses of dashes

Explanation

One **dash** can be used to add an extra thought or piece of information to the **end of a sentence**. This is particularly useful if you want to create an **exciting or humorous pause**.

Example Now Theo was as rich as the king himself – **maybe richer**!

Activities

1 Rewrite these sentences adding a **dash** between **clauses** to make the sentence more effective.

a He was frightened-more frightened than he had ever been before.

He was frightened - more frightened than he had ever been before.

b The machine was going crazy it was completely out of control.

The machine was going crazy - it was completely out of control.

c Everyone thought David was mad-everyone except Martha.

Everyone thought David was mad - everyone except Martha.

2 Use a dash to add a **comment** or **extra information** to the end of each sentence. Make it something dramatic, amusing or surprising.

a There was only one thing for it – go beserk

b He opened the classroom door – Surprised to hear "You're late!"

c Down the road came the runaway car – it was going at at least 6omph

d You should have seen his face – It was hilarious

e The battle was finally won – by the minority, who had won 1,000 to 500

Did you know?

The word '**dash**' means 'a hasty stroke of the pen.' The dash was originally used when writing quickly. Today, dashes are still used mainly in more informal writing. In formal writing, commas, colons and semicolons are used to separate clauses, rather than dashes.

Colons

Explanation

A **colon** can be used when you **introduce** (or lead into) **a quotation**, **an example** or a **piece of information**.

Example Dad has a favourite saying: **There's no smoke without fire.** ← quotation

For example: **owls are nocturnal.** ← example

Here is the issue: **we have no apples.** ← information

Activities

1 Add a **colon** to the end of these sentences. Then finish each sentence by adding the necessary **extra information**.

a Here is my new address : 312 ork road SW12 FGB.

b The judges had reached a decision : John was the winner.

c I read the headline in Dad's paper : Brocoli is forbidden.

d The warning on the sign was clear : Warning, Do not enter.

e Let me tell you something about Joe : His favourite sport is Hockey

f My message to you is this : When you sit on a toilet, sit on the seat.

Colons are used **between two main clauses** if the second statement helps **explain or expand on** the first.

Example The weather forecast was wrong: **it rained all day**.

Each statement is a main clause so you cannot use a comma between them.

---

2 Insert the colon in the appropriate place in the sentences below.

a We have a problem : the front tyre is flat.

b There is no way home : the roads are completely flooded.

c We were exhausted : the journey had taken all night.

d We must take care of Alice : she is only four.

e Icy pavements can be dangerous : people frequently slip and fall.

Semicolons

Semicolons are used to separate **two** sentences (or **main clauses**) together, rather than using a conjunction. The two sentences must be closely linked or related. Semicolons are particularly useful for **balancing two pieces of information**.

Example The red team were the winners**;** **the blues** were exhausted.

A comma cannot be used between two sentences, but the stronger semicolon can.

Activities

1 Rewrite each pair of sentences as **one sentence**. Use a **semicolon** to link the two clauses.

a Elizabeth I was born in 1533. She died in 1603.

Elizabeth I was born in 1533; She died in 1603.

b The soup was excellent. The rest of the meal was disappointing.

The soup was excellent; The rest of the meal was disappointing.

c Outside the storm raged. Inside it was snug and cosy.

Outside the storm raged; inside it was snug and cosy

d The home team were winning. The visitors were struggling.

The home team were winning; The visitors were struggling.

e My favourite flavour is mint-choc chip. Jess prefers strawberry shortcake.

My favourite flavour is mint-choc chip; Jess prefers strawberry shortcake.

2 Insert a semicolon in the correct place in the sentences below.

a It was autumn; the days were getting shorter.

b My baby brother sleeps with the light on; he hates the dark.

c He had trained hard; he was ready for the race.

d He looked in the box; it was empty.

e The house had been empty for years; it was a terrible mess.

f I want to visit Italy; it is supposed to be lovely.

Colons and semicolons in lists

A **colon** can also be used to **introduce a list**.

Example We made five different sorts of sandwiches: **jam, cheese, ham, salad and chicken**.

The statement before the colon makes sense on its own.

1 Add a **colon** to the end of these sentences. Then finish each sentence by adding a **list**. The first one has been done for you.

a Humans have three types of teeth : canines, incisors and molars.

b You will need to bring with you the following items : ruchsack; camping bag; book; jacket; boots and clothes.

c There are many different types of bread : rye; sourdough; white and many, many more.

d Everything they had was lost in the fire : maps; gloves; coat and the ruchsack

Like commas, **semicolons** can be used to **separate items** in a **list**. Use semicolons, rather than commas, in a list of **longer phrases**, especially if the phrases **include** commas.

Example It was a fabulous picnic: freshly baked bread**;** delicious pastries**;** ripe, juicy peaches**;** loads of tea and bottles of ice-cold lemonade.

2 Insert the **colon** and **semicolons** into this sentence.

The following children were elected to School Council: Sophie Hughes, Class 3; James Dawson, Class 4; Lee Douglas, Class 5; Aisha Khan, Class 6.

3 Complete this sentence by adding a list of suitable phrases separated by semicolons.

Many things help make a good holiday: skiing; nice food; sun; camping; swiming and last but not least, adventure.

Bullet points

Explanation

Sometimes **ideas or items** are **listed** and presented as **bullet points**.

Example Your picnic might include: ← colon (after the introductory statement)

- freshly baked bread
- delicious pastries
- ripe, juicy peaches
- loads of tea
- ice-cold lemonade. ← full stop (ending the final bullet point)

Sometimes a **semicolon** is used at the end of each bullet point (except the last one). The most important thing is to decide how you are going to punctuate your bullet points then stick to it.

Activities

1 Write a **bullet point** list describing the features of your dream hotel.

The hotel has everything you could wish for, including:

- <u>a splash pool for children</u>
- <u>two large saunas</u>
- <u>a restraunt with fastfood and other types</u>
- <u>an ice-skating rink</u>

Sometimes each **bullet point** is a **complete sentence**. In this case, each sentence should start with a **capital letter** and end with a **full stop**.

---

2 Complete this bullet point list using **complete sentences**. The first one has been done for you.

- Capital letters <u>show the start of a sentence.</u>
- Full stops <u>Show the end of a sentence</u>.
- Question marks <u>Show the end of a question</u>.
- Exclamation marks <u>Show the end of an exclamation</u>.

Hyphens 1

Explanation

A **hyphen** looks like a short dash. It is used to **link words** together, rather than parts of a sentence. It shows that the words should be read **together**.

Example It was a child-friendly hotel.

Here the hyphen shows that the word 'child' is linked to the word 'friendly' to make a phrase that describes the hotel. It is a hotel that welcomes children.

Activities

1 Look at the words in the box. Find **pairs of words** that could be joined together with a **hyphen**. Write the words on the list. The first one has been done for you.

down	man	light	raising
sugar	full	upside	free
hair	hearted	eating	length

a upside-down cake

b Sugar-free drink

c man-eating shark

d full-length mirror

e hair raising adventure

f light-hearted story

2 Underline the words in each of these sentences that should be linked with a hyphen. Then write the words as they would appear with a hyphen.

a Angus proved to be a right know it all.

b Jenny is my sports mad sister.

c The concert was jam packed with fans.

d There had been a break in at the garage.

e Mike has always been rather heavy handed.

f Mrs Cardell did not get on with her daughter in law.

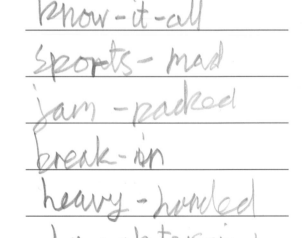

know-it-all
sports-mad
jam-packed
break-in
heavy-handed
daughter-in-law

Punctuation

Hyphens 2

Explanation

Using a **hyphen** can help to make your meaning clear and **avoid confusion** or **ambiguity**.

Example a little used bicycle.

→ a little, used bicycle (little and used)   a little-used bicycle **?** (not much used)

In the last example, the hyphen shows that 'little' and 'used' go together to give one phrase to describe the bicycle – it has not been used much.

Activities

1 Is a **comma** or a **hyphen** the most likely punctuation in these phrases? Add the **correct punctuation** in each box. Then copy the phrase correctly.

a a cold [,] windy day _a cold, windy day_

b a blue [–] eyed youngster _a blue-eyed youngster_

c a kind [–] hearted man _a kind-hearted man_

d a dark [,] damp dungeon _a dark, damp dungeon_

e a long [–] winded story _a long-winded story_

f a lean [,] hungry dog _a lean, hungry dog_

2 Underline the word(s) where a **hyphen** would help to make the **meaning clear**. (In some cases this may be a single word that needs splitting up.) Then write the underlined word(s) correctly.

a The club is open to all <u>seven year old</u> children. _Seven-year-old_

b A <u>man eating</u> monster stalked the town. _man-eating_

c The case was bulging with <u>twenty pound</u> notes. _twenty-pound_

d I'll recover the old <u>sofa</u> with this red fabric. _sofa-_

e Dad had to <u>resign his</u> smudged signature. _re-sign_

Did you know?

Lots of words once written with a hyphen are now written as one compound word – for example, 'playground' and 'bumblebee'. The word 'e-mail' is also now more commonly written as 'email'.

Proofreading 4

1 Write this sentence with the **brackets** in the correct place.

Mrs Jenkins the head teacher always takes assembly (on Monday mornings).

Mrs Jenkins (the head teacher) always takes assembly on Monday mornings.

2 Insert **commas** and a **semicolon** to punctuate the sentence below.

On the one hand, a holiday in Jamaica would be great; on the other hand, it is really expensive.

3 Write a sentence using a **colon** that lists vehicles stuck in a traffic jam.

Hundreds of vehicles were *these ones: 120 cars, 89 vans, 12 lorries, 3 taxis and 12 bikes.*

4 Rewrite this text, adding punctuation to make the meaning clear. Try to use the full range of punctuation to make it more effective.

what will life be like in the future in 100 years will the world look the same of course we cannot know for sure but we can make some predictions cities of the future might look very different perhaps even unrecognisable people might live in pods rather than houses vehicles might travel on rails above the ground rather than on roads because of pollution people might wear masks and protective clothing just think how IT computers email the internet has already changed our lives

What will life be in the future? In 100 years? Will the world look the same? Of course we cannot know for sure but we can make some predictions. Cities of the future might look very different, perhaps even unrecognisable. People might live in pods rather than houses, vehicles might travel on rails above the ground rather than on the road. Because of pollution, people might wear masks and protective clothing. Just think how IT computers email. The internet has changed our lives.

Write a quiz

Write a quiz for your friends. Choose a subject that you know a lot about and think up 10 questions. Write the questions on a sheet of paper with spaces for the answers. Remember to use question marks at the end of each question.

Punctuation collage

Look through comics, newspapers and books. Find examples of sentences using different punctuation marks. Cut or copy them out and stick them on a piece of paper to make a collage.

Punctuation placemat

Make a punctuation placemat with a picture made up of different punctuation marks (for example, a face with a question-mark nose or an alien with exclamation marks for antennae). Use the placemat to help remember the different types of punctuation when you are writing.

It's a joke!

Collect together all your favourite jokes and make a joke book. Lots of jokes are in the form of questions, so remember to use question marks for these and exclamation marks for the punchline. You might also need to use commas and dashes.

Showstopper sentence

A 'showstopper sentence' shows off your best punctuation. It might use a semicolon or a dash, or include something in brackets. Impress your parents, friends and teachers – include a showstopper sentence in every piece of writing you do.

Be possessive

Make labels for your important possessions at school and home (for example, Ben's room, Kelly's diary). Make sure you put the possessive apostrophe in the right place.

What a photograph

Write one-sentence captions to accompany your family photographs, giving details about dates, people, places and events. Remember to use capital letters for names of people, places and months of the year. Decide whether and where you need commas in your sentences.

Answers

Page 4: Full stops and capital letters 1

1 **a** The old man waited. The bus was very late.

  b Triangles have three sides and squares have four.

  c The sky was blue. It was a lovely day.

  d The boy was late. His teacher was angry.

  e My best friend is 11 and I am nearly 10.

  f Ducks have webbed feet to help them swim.

2 These are just examples. You might have thought of different sentences.

  a The firefighters **rushed into the burning building. They had to rescue the trapped child.**

  b A man appeared carrying **a large box. He put it on the table.**

  c Cinderella **sat all alone in the cold kitchen. She was feeling very sad.**

  d Plants need **water to live. They also need sunlight to help them to grow.**

Page 5: Full stops and capital letters 2

1 **a** My older sister likes to play very loud music. My little sister spends all her time glued to the television or reading comics.

  b We are having a lovely time. The weather has been great all week.

  c Anil walked towards the door. He felt the rusty handle. The door was locked.

  d Many trees lose their leaves in autumn. This helps the tree to survive the winter.

  e Sunny Sands has many exciting places for you to visit. A great place to start is the beach with its many attractions.

Page 6: Questions and question marks

1 **a** How do you feel today**?**   **d** Why does the wind blow**?**

  b Is this your dog**?**   **e** I can swim a length of the pool.

  c You will really like this new game.   **f** Do you think we can win this match**?**

2 These are just examples of questions you might ask. Make sure you have used a question mark.

  a What do **you like to do?**   **d** Why have **you moved here?**

  b Where did **you live before?**   **e** How many **brothers and sisters do you have?**

  c When is **your birthday?**

Page 7: Exclamations and exclamation marks

1 **a** I went to school.   **d** My best friend has dyed her hair bright pink!

  b Suddenly everyone shouted HAPPY BIRTHDAY!   **e** Great prizes to be won!

  c My best friend lives in the house next door.   **f** Sweets are bad for your teeth.

2 **a** Oh dear!   **b** Ouch!   **c** What a mess!   **d** Help!

Page 8: Other uses of capital letters

1 This is just an example to show where you should have used capital letters.

My name is **Kerry Meadows**. I live in **Manchester**. My birthday is in **July**. My teacher is **Mr Kendall**. My favourite television programme is **Doctor Who**.

2 **a** Turn right into Cedar Road and walk as far as St George's School.

b Meet Tess outside Spendless Supermarket on Monday.

c Amelia Earhart flew across the Atlantic Ocean in May 1932.

d The author Philip Ridley was born in London. As well as being an author, he is also an artist. He studied painting at St Martin's School of Art. Some of his most famous books are *Meteorite Spoon*, *Krindlekrax* and *Mercedes Ice*.

Page 9: Proofreading 1

1 Dear Alice

Thank you for the birthday card. I'm sorry to hear about your cold. Are you feeling better now? You missed a great party on Saturday. Shall I tell you about it? We had a disco in the garden and then a barbecue. Everyone joined in with dancing on the grass. The funniest moment was when Ben Stokes fell in the pond! It was hilarious!

2 Are you fed up with the same boring breakfast cereal? Then try new Frosty Fruity Flakes. It's the fruit with a crunch! You will simply love these golden flakes of crunchy corn. They come packed with the flavour of real fruit and taste just great. Go on, start your day with a true fruit boost!

Page 10: Commas in lists

1 **a** For a healthy start to the day, try having fruit juice, low sugar cereal, wholemeal toast and some fresh fruit.

b You will need two pieces of card, a sharp pencil, some glue, felt tip pens and a pair of scissors.

c Try adding grated cheese, slices of pepper, mushrooms, chopped ham and sweetcorn to the top of your pizza.

d The book includes short stories from famous authors such as Nina Bawden, Michael Morpurgo, Rose Impey and Joan Aiken.

e Leo's lost kitten was not in the kitchen, the living room, the garage or the cupboard under the stairs.

2 These are just suggestions. You might have included other items in your lists.

a In the old lady's handbag there was a leather diary, **a red purse, a scented envelope, a book of stamps and a bus pass**.

b In the treasure chest we found **fabulous jewellery, gold coins, silver ornaments and a very old map**.

c On planet Zelg we saw **amazing blue plants, huge craters, strange pools of slime and an alien spaceship**.

Page 11: Apostrophes: omission

1
a	isn't	**e**	doesn't
b	I'd	**f**	you're
c	shouldn't	**g**	I'll
d	we've	**h**	Jenna's

2 'Kavita! **I've** been looking everywhere for you,' exclaimed Michael. 'Come on, **we'll** have to run. **It's** late.'

'**I'm** not running. I **don't** care if **we're** late,' said Kavita in disgust.

'**It'll** be your fault if we miss the start of the concert. **They've** probably started already. We promised **we'd** be there.'

Page 12: Apostrophes: possession

1
a	the monster's teeth	**d**	the castle's walls
b	Jack's beanstalk	**e**	the author's first book
c	Tarik's CDs		

2

the chefs' hats	the footballers' shorts
the doctors' surgery	the children's playground
the teachers' staffroom	the soldiers' uniforms

Page 13: Apostrophes: confusions

1
a	DVDs for sale	**e**	children's clothes
b	Jean's café	**f**	Opens Sundays
c	No cameras allowed	**g**	Stella's cupcakes
d	Teas and coffees	**h**	Ted's taxis

2
a	That's **Kates'** bag next to yours.	Kate's
b	The dog can't find **it's** owner.	its
c	Joe's left his bag in the **mens'** changing room.	men's
d	Mrs Potter's parrot escaped from **it's** cage.	its
e	The sweets weren't **her's**.	hers
f	That's Grandma's tea but **its** gone cold.	it's
g	**Micks** parents brought him to ours.	Mick's

Page 14: Inverted commas 1

1
a 'That was fun!' exclaimed Simeon.

b 'Aah, peace at last,' sighed Maya.

c 'What do you think you're doing?' demanded Mr Jenkins.

d 'We will have to jump!' shouted Kelly.

Page 15: Inverted commas 2

1 **a** Simeon exclaimed, 'That was fun!'

b Maya sighed, 'Aah, peace at last.'

c Mr Jenkins demanded, 'What do you think you're doing?'

d Kelly shouted, 'We will have to jump!'

2 **a** Mr Henderson asked, 'Are we ready to go?'

b Suddenly, a voice shouted, 'Look out below!'

c 'Where are you going?' asked Ellie. 'It will be dark soon.'

d The captain announced, 'We sail tomorrow.'

e 'It's nearly home time,' said Miss Achebe. 'Let's tidy up.'

f Sam shouted, 'Wait for me,' as he ran after the bus. (Or: 'Wait for me!')

Page 16: Setting out direct speech

1 This is just an example of how the conversation might look as direct speech.

'Excuse me, young man, but can you spare a few coins so that I can buy a little bread for my supper?' croaked the old lady.

'I am sorry, but I too am very poor and have no money,' explained Jack, sadly. 'All I have in the world is my cow Daisy and I am taking her to market.'

The old lady was about to go on her way when Jack had an idea …

'Why don't you take Daisy to market?'

'Oh I couldn't,' said the old lady.

'But you must. Your need is greater than mine,' insisted Jack.

'Well, I am very hungry,' said the old lady. 'Yes, I will take your cow. But only if you take these magic beans in return.'

Page 17: Proofreading 2

1 **a** We're too busy. ☐O omission **d** Zoe's forgotten me. ☐P omission

b I am Marie's best friend. ☐P possession **e** She's late again. ☐O omission

c It was his father's voice. ☐P possession **f** Look in the dog's basket. ☐P possession

2 **b** Suddenly, a voice shouted, 'Everyone get down!'

3 'When did you have it last?' asked Lara.

'I'm not sure,' said Guy, searching through his pockets.

'Perhaps it's at Simon's house,' suggested Max.

'I don't think so,' said Guy. 'I never took it out.'

'Can you remember dropping it?' asked Max.

'Got it!' shouted Guy, holding up a key. 'It must've dropped through the lining.'

4 Gran wore a checked woollen skirt, a flowery blouse, a pink cardigan, a patterned headscarf and blue fluffy slippers.

Page 18: Commas: separation 1

1 a **Slowly**, I woke from a deep sleep.

    b **Next**, attach the string.

    c **Suddenly**, the sun came out.

    d **Finally**, the rain has stopped.

    e **Anyway**, it worked out fine.

    f **Tomorrow**, we leave for Spain.

    g **Eagerly**, she opened the box.

2 a **On Saturday morning,** the family went shopping.

    b **Before the concert,** the orchestra tuned up.

    c **On holiday,** we swam every day.

    d **In last night's gale,** all the bins blew over.

    e **At 5 o'clock,** the coach will leave London.

    f **By the next morning,** the storm was over.

Page 19: Commas: separation 2

1 a No, that can't be right.

    b Stella, is that you?

    c Ah well, that's my work done for today.

    d Yes, he was sure this was the place.

    e You can stop that right now, Martin.

    f Oh dear, we seem to have forgotten something.

    g Sarah and Michael, I'm talking to you.

2 a He's very late, isn't he?

    b That's a beautiful sight, **isn't it?**

    c They are the best team, **aren't they?**

    d We will win, **won't we?**

    e You do believe me, **don't you?**

    f You're Ben's friend, **aren't you?**

Page 20: Commas: subordinate clauses 1

1 a Marcia watched the world become smaller **as** she zoomed into the sky.

    b The box was heavy **although** it was only small.

    c Henry VIII was King of England from 1509 **until** he died in 1547.

    d It is important to eat lots of fruit and vegetables **because** they contain vitamins.

    e Carrie paused for a moment **before** she entered the room.

2 a Stacey enjoys all sports, especially playing tennis.

    b Max was late, which really annoyed James.

    c Everyone agreed to try, yet no-one would go first.

Page 21: Commas: subordinate clauses 2

1 a **When the spaceship landed,** I escaped from the aliens.

    b **If it rains all day,** we will have to stay inside.

    c **Because the roads were flooded,** the journey took longer than expected.

    d **Although I had a map,** we were soon completely lost.

    e **As darkness fell,** they continued to hunt for survivors.

2 These are just examples.

   a While **we were playing outside,** your dog ate the birthday cake.

   b When **the fire went out,** I went to bed.

   c As **the aeroplane roared overhead,** everyone looked up.

   d Although **it was late,** he followed the others.

Page 22: Commas: subordinate clauses 3

1 These are just examples of how you might have completed the sentences.

   a Running frantically, the man shouted for help.

   b Grabbing the steering wheel, **she tried to get control of the car**.

   c Trembling nervously**, he stepped forward**.

   d Amazed by what she had seen, **Fatima walked thoughtfully home**.

   e Moving cautiously, **they made their way through the forest**.

   f Watched by the others, **Mark began to climb the tree**.

2 **a** **Finding a trail of footprints,** Millie followed them.

   b **Looking through the window,** Nick saw everything.

   c The clock struck midnight**, making Cinderella jump**.

   d The wind blew fiercely, **forcing Hassan back**.

   e The phone rang suddenly, **startling Mrs Bishop**.

Page 23: Commas: clarifying meaning

1 **a** Standing next to her uncle, Sam felt tiny.

   b It must be nearly time to eat, Dad.

   c The dragon had large, bright green wings.

   d Most of the time, travellers were happy with the service.

   e They had 50 model cars, each in its original box.

2 **b** Seeing the creature so close, Kelly grew anxious.

   d Varsha opened the door a little, peering into the darkness.

   e As it was dark inside, the children could see nothing.

Page 24: Commas and full stops

1 **a** Shining the torch into the darkness, Sara could just make out a small figure. ✓

   b As soon as she heard the scream, Cal rushed downstairs. ✓

   c The man asked Carlos for some help. Carlos ignored him. ✗

   d Henry VIII had six wives. Catherine of Aragon was Henry's first wife. ✗

   e Looking out of the plane, we could see the patchwork of fields below us. ✓

   f Heat the oven to 180°C. Place the biscuits on a baking tray. ✗

2 Glowing fiercely, the spaceship hovered just overhead. While it was really quite close to us, it was almost impossible to see anything because of the light. We had to shield our eyes.
(Or: Because of the light, we had to shield our eyes.)

Page 25: Proofreading 3

1 a The boys **couldn't** find either of **Tim's** sisters.

b Tim's needs an apostrophe for possession – they are his sisters.

couldn't needs an apostrophe for omission to show missing letters in a contraction.

2 As he passed the school gates, he began thinking about Mrs Walker, Suzie and the other pupils.

3 When I saw the ma**n c**oming towards me, I felt afraid. **W**e both stopped, waiting for each other to move.

4 Some slight variation in the use of commas is possible.

'What's that in your hand**?**' asked **S**adie.

'Nothing,' replied **M**ark, clearly startled**.**

'Why are you hiding it then**?**' pressed **S**adie. 'I know you're up to something**.'**

'It's mine,' **M**ark muttered defensively**.**

'Come on, hand it over, little brother,' said **S**adie, grabbing her brother's clenched fist**.**

Page 26: Parenthesis: commas

1 a Mr Richardson, **the headteacher,** was pleased with the response.

b Sheila Jenks, **aged 50,** was recovering last night in hospital.

c The man, **smiling to himself,** put the money in his pocket.

d Mrs Patel, **who was rather old,** had to sit down to rest.

e The cottage, **which is empty,** stands on the edge of the village.

f Sam, **although the youngest,** was a worthy winner.

2 a Mr Reynolds, the teacher, spoke to the class.

b Miss Mystical, the magician, performed her vanishing trick.

c Molly, my little sister, is six years old.

d Zoe Star, the singer, performed her latest hit.

e Snowflake, the white cat, was stuck in the oak tree.

Page 27: Parenthesis: brackets

1 a We tried two flavours **(orange and strawberry)** but didn't like either.

b Animals have to be able to hide from their predators **(the animals that hunt them)** in order to survive.

c The survey found that most people **(almost 70% of those asked)** would like to see the playground kept open.

d Make sure you leave a small opening at the top **(see Diagram 2)**.

e All carnivores **(meat eaters)** have sharp teeth.

f Nikki **(who lives next door)** rushed to our rescue.

2 These are just examples. You may have included other comments or information in the brackets.

  a In the bath **(just looking up at me)** was the biggest spider I'd ever seen.

  b I have two rabbits **(called Benny and Bobtail)**, a dog and a goldfish.

  c Ali **(who had set off first)** was last to finish.

  d Mum **(forgetful as ever)** left the tap running.

  e Mr Martin's new car **(the red Ferrari)** was stolen on Monday.

  f We grew all sorts of vegetables **(carrots, peas, beans, cabbages)** in our garden.

Page 28: Parenthesis: dashes

1 **a** My father – **not the greatest cook** – made pizza for everyone.

  b Just one more lesson – **PE with Mr Roberts** – before home time.

  c James – **who was bored** – thought it was time to leave.

  d The dragon – **a huge, scaly beast** – emerged from the cave.

  e His choice of clothes – **a T-shirt and jeans** – seemed out of place.

2 These are just examples. You may have included other comments between the dashes.

  a Mrs Hopkins – **grumpy as ever** – complained about the noise.

  b Jodie – **who is the brainy one** – won the competition.

  c Our new teacher – **quite young and funny** – is called Mr Groves.

  d Dad was in the kitchen – **preparing dinner** – when they arrived.

  e Harry's model – **made from old bicycle parts** – was clearly the best.

Page 29: Other uses of dashes

1 **a** He was frightened – more frightened than he had ever been before.

  b The machine was going crazy – it was completely out of control.

  c Everyone thought David was mad – everyone except Martha.

2 These are examples. You may have added different endings.

  a There was only one thing for it – **run**!

  b He opened the classroom door – **it was empty**.

  c Down the road came the runaway car – **no-one could stop it**.

  d You should have seen his face – **it was a picture**!

  e The battle was finally won – **but at great cost**.

Page 30: Colons

1 These are just examples. You may have ended the sentences in different ways.

   a Here is my new address**: 6, Walnut Lane, Melchester.**

   b The judges had reached a decision**: he was through to the final.**

   c I read the headline in Dad's paper**: Lion escapes from zoo.**

   d The warning on the sign was clear**: DANGER – KEEP OUT!**

   e Let me tell you something about Joe**: he is completely mad**.

   f My message to you is this**: I will never surrender.**

2 **a** We have a problem: the front tyre is flat.

   b There is no way home: the roads are completely flooded.

   c We were exhausted: the journey had taken all night.

   d We must take care of Alice: she is only four.

   e Icy pavements can be dangerous: people frequently slip and fall.

Page 31: Semicolons

1 **a** Elizabeth I was born in 1533; she died in 1603.

   b The soup was excellent; the rest of the meal was disappointing.

   c Outside the storm raged; inside it was snug and cosy.

   d The home team were winning; the visitors were struggling.

   e My favourite flavour is mint-choc chip; Jess prefers strawberry shortcake.

2 **a** It was autumn; the days were getting shorter.

   b My baby brother sleeps with the light on; he hates the dark.

   c He had trained hard; he was ready for the race.

   d He looked in the box; it was empty.

   e The house had been empty for years; it was a terrible mess.

   f I want to visit Italy; it is supposed to be lovely.

Page 32: Colons and semicolons in lists

1 These are just examples. You may have ended the sentences in different ways.

   a Humans have three types of teeth: canines, incisors and molars.

   b You will need to bring with you the following items: **boots, a waterproof coat, a drink and a packed lunch**.

   c There are many different types of bread: **white, wholemeal, soda bread, pitta bread and chapattis**.

   d Everything they had was lost in the fire: **furniture, clothes, books and toys**.

2 The following children were elected to School Council: Sophie Hughes, Class 3; James Dawson, Class 4; Lee Douglas, Class 5; Aisha Khan, Class 6.

3 This is just an example. You may have added other suitable phrases.

Many things help make a good holiday: great sandy beaches; interesting places to visit; plenty to do; a smart, reasonably priced hotel; good food **and** lovely weather.

Page 33: Bullet points

1 These are just examples. Your list may have different features.
The hotel has everything you could wish for, including:
- a splash pool for children
- **a magnificent sun terrace**
- **a relaxing spa area**
- **an award-winning restaurant**.

2 These are examples. Your sentences may be slightly different.
- Capital letters show the start of a sentence.
- Full stops **show the end of a sentence**.
- Question marks **go at the end of a question**.
- Exclamation marks **go at the end of an exclamation**.

Page 34: Hyphens 1

1
- **a** upside-down cake
- **b** sugar-free drink
- **c** man-eating shark
- **d** full-length mirror
- **e** hair-raising adventure
- **f** light-hearted story

2
- **a** Angus proved to be a right **know it all**.   know-it-all
- **b** Jenny is my **sports mad** sister   sports-mad
- **c** The concert was **jam packed** with fans.   jam-packed
- **d** There had been a **break in** at the garage.   break-in
- **e** Mike has always been rather **heavy handed**.   heavy-handed
- **f** Mrs Cardell did not get on with her **daughter in law**.   daughter-in-law

Page 35: Hyphens 2

1
- **a** a cold, windy day
- **b** a blue-eyed youngster
- **c** a kind-hearted man
- **d** a dark, damp dungeon
- **e** a long-winded story
- **f** a lean, hungry dog

2
- **a** The club is open to all **seven year old** children.   seven-year-old
- **b** A **man eating** monster stalked the town.   man-eating
- **c** The case was bulging with **twenty pound** notes.   twenty-pound
- **d** I'll **recover** the old sofa with this red fabric.   re-cover
- **e** Dad had to **resign** his smudged signature.   re-sign

Page 36· Proofreading 4

1 Mrs Jenkins **(the head teacher)** always takes assembly on Monday mornings.

2 On the one hand, a holiday in Jamaica would be great; on the other hand, it is really expensive.

3 This is just an example of the sort of sentence you might have written.

Hundreds of vehicles were **stuck in the traffic jam: cars, lorries, buses, delivery vans and even a tractor**.

4 Some variations are possible in your choice of commas, brackets or dashes.

What will life be like in the future? **I**n 100 years, will the world look the same? **O**f course, we cannot know for sure – but we can make some predictions.

Cities of the future might look very different – perhaps, even unrecognisable. **P**eople might live in pods rather than houses; vehicles might travel on rails above the ground rather than on roads. **B**ecause of pollution, people might wear masks and protective clothing.

Just think how IT **(**computers, email, the internet**)** has already changed our lives.